Contents

Links to Abacus weekly plans

This information is for teachers who want to see how the Mastery Checkpoints are planned into the Abacus maths programme.

Autumn term 1		
Week 2	Checkpoint 1	Place value in 4-digit numbers
Week 3	Checkpoint 2	Times-tables facts
Week 3	Checkpoint 3	Finding fractions of amounts
Week 4	Checkpoint 4	Telling the time

Autumn term 2		
Week 6	Checkpoint 5	Doubling and halving 3-digit numbers
Week 7	Checkpoint 6	Adding 3-digit numbers in columns
Week 7	Checkpoint 7	Finding tenths
Week 8	Checkpoint 8	Converting measures
Week 9	Checkpoint 9	Counting up to solve subtraction
Week 10	Checkpoint 10	Multiplying with a grid

Spring term 1		
Week 11	Checkpoint 11	Rounding 3 and 4-digit numbers
Week 11	Checkpoint 12	Adding and subtracting multiples of 1, 10 and 100
Week 13	Checkpoint 13	Solving problems with fractions
Week 13	Checkpoint 14	Finding equivalent fractions
Week 14	Checkpoint 15	Acute and obtuse angles
Week 14	Checkpoint 16	Identifying symmetry in shapes
Week 15	Checkpoint 17	Dividing 2- and 3-digit numbers
Week 15	Checkpoint 18	All the multiplication and division facts

Spring term 2		
Week 17	Checkpoint 19	Addition methods
Week 17	Checkpoint 20	Different subtraction methods
Week 18	Checkpoint 21	Converting clock times
Week 20	Checkpoint 22	Solving addition and subtraction problems

Summer term 1		
Week 21	Checkpoint 23	Negative numbers
Week 23	Checkpoint 24	Mental multiplication and division
Week 23	Checkpoint 25	Setting out and solving multiplication problems
Week 24	Checkpoint 26	Finding the area and perimeter of shapes
Week 24	Checkpoint 27	Properties of shapes
Week 25	Checkpoint 28	Counting and solving problems with decimals
Week 25	Checkpoint 29	Simplifying and comparing fractions

Summer term 2		
Week 26	Checkpoint 30	Mental addition using place value and number facts
Week 26	Checkpoint 31	Solving problems using multiplication and factors
Week 27	Checkpoint 32	Solving and checking subtraction problems
Week 28	Checkpoint 33	Using coordinates
Week 28	Checkpoint 34	Using information in a bar chart
Week 29	Checkpoint 35	Adding and subtracting fractions
Week 29	Checkpoint 36	Multiplying and dividing decimals
Week 30	Checkpoint 37	Finding fractional amounts

How to use this book

Mastery Checkpoints

The Mastery Checkpoints give you a chance to show how much you have learned about a key maths skill, straight after you have learned about it in lessons.

Each Checkpoint starts with a few questions for everyone to try. These are followed by some more in-depth questions in the Champions' Challenge section.

The title tells you which skill the Checkpoint is about.

Read each question carefully!

The Champions' Challenge section gives you more challenging questions.

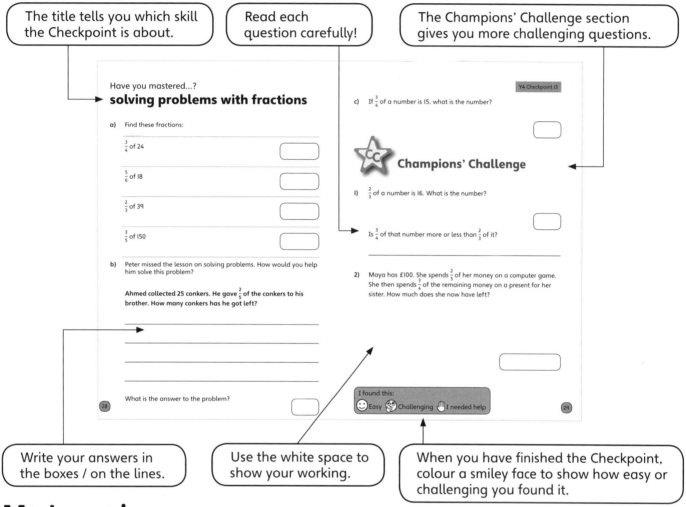

Have you mastered...?
solving problems with fractions

a) Find these fractions:

$\frac{3}{4}$ of 24

$\frac{5}{6}$ of 18

$\frac{2}{3}$ of 39

$\frac{3}{5}$ of 150

b) Peter missed the lesson on solving problems. How would you help him solve this problem?

Ahmed collected 25 conkers. He gave $\frac{2}{5}$ of the conkers to his brother. How many conkers has he got left?

What is the answer to the problem?

Y4 Checkpoint 13

c) If $\frac{3}{4}$ of a number is 15, what is the number?

Champions' Challenge

1) $\frac{2}{3}$ of a number is 16. What is the number?

Is $\frac{3}{4}$ of that number more or less than $\frac{2}{3}$ of it?

2) Maya has £100. She spends $\frac{2}{5}$ of her money on a computer game. She then spends $\frac{3}{4}$ of the remaining money on a present for her sister. How much does she now have left?

I found this:
😊 Easy 🤔 Challenging ✋ I needed help

Write your answers in the boxes / on the lines.

Use the white space to show your working.

When you have finished the Checkpoint, colour a smiley face to show how easy or challenging you found it.

My Learning

On pages 80–85 you will find opportunities for you to reflect on your own learning: for example, challenges you have faced and how you tackled them, useful mistakes you have made and how they helped you to learn, and ways you might use the skills you have learned in real life. Your teacher will tell you when to complete each of these pages.

My Mastery

On pages 86–91 you will find tables that list the Checkpoint skills, and give you a chance to re-assess how confident you feel about each of them later in the year. Your teacher will tell you when to complete these self-assessments, for example, at the end of each half-term.

Have you mastered...?
place value in 4-digit numbers

a) Match these five numbers to the right positions, A – E.

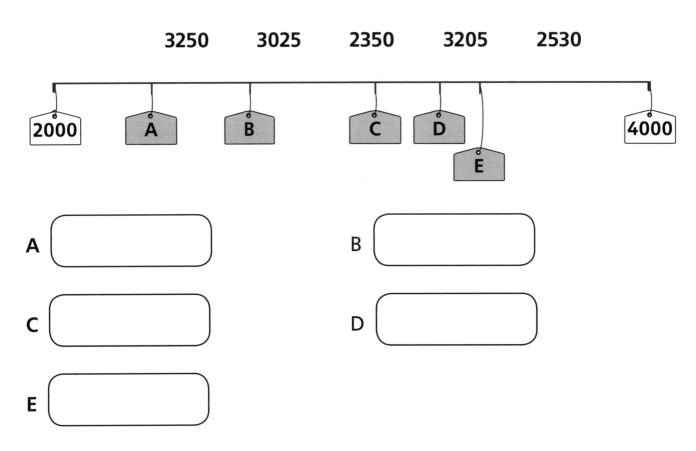

3250   3025   2350   3205   2530

A [   ]   B [   ]

C [   ]   D [   ]

E [   ]

b) What number could go between:
A and B?

D and E?

[   ]

Champions' Challenge

Using only the four digits 3, 5, 5 and 8, make at least six different 4-digit numbers. Put them in order from smallest to largest.

Have you mastered...?
times-tables facts

Solve the following:

a)   4 × 8 = [ ]

b)   42 ÷ 6 = [ ]

c)   9 × [ ] = 45

d)   [ ] ÷ 8 = 8

e)   7 × 9 = [ ]

f)   48 ÷ 8 = [ ]

g)   30 × 6 = [ ]

h)   70 × 4 = [ ]

Champions' Challenge

1)   Find three different times-table facts that give an answer of 24.

2)   Find three different times-table facts that give an answer of 36.

3)   Find three different multiplication facts that you can multiply by 10 to give an answer of 600.

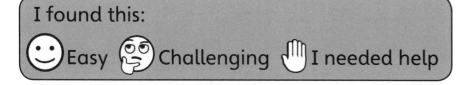

I found this:

😊 Easy   🤔 Challenging   ✋ I needed help

Have you mastered...?
finding fractions of amounts

Find these fractions:

a) $\frac{1}{4}$ of 36

b) $\frac{1}{6}$ of 72

c) $\frac{1}{3}$ of 39

d) $\frac{1}{5}$ of 500

e) $\frac{1}{8}$ of 48

Champions' Challenge

1) Peter says that $\frac{1}{6}$ of 54 kg is heavier than $\frac{1}{4}$ of 48 kg.
   Is he right?

   _____

   How can you check?

   _____

2) Is $\frac{1}{5}$ of 55 kg heavier or lighter than $\frac{1}{6}$ of 54 kg?

   _____

   Is it heavier or lighter than $\frac{1}{4}$ of 48 kg?   _____

3) Write a unit fraction of 60 kg that would be lighter than any of the above.

   _____

I found this:

 Easy   Challenging    I needed help

Have you mastered...?
telling the time

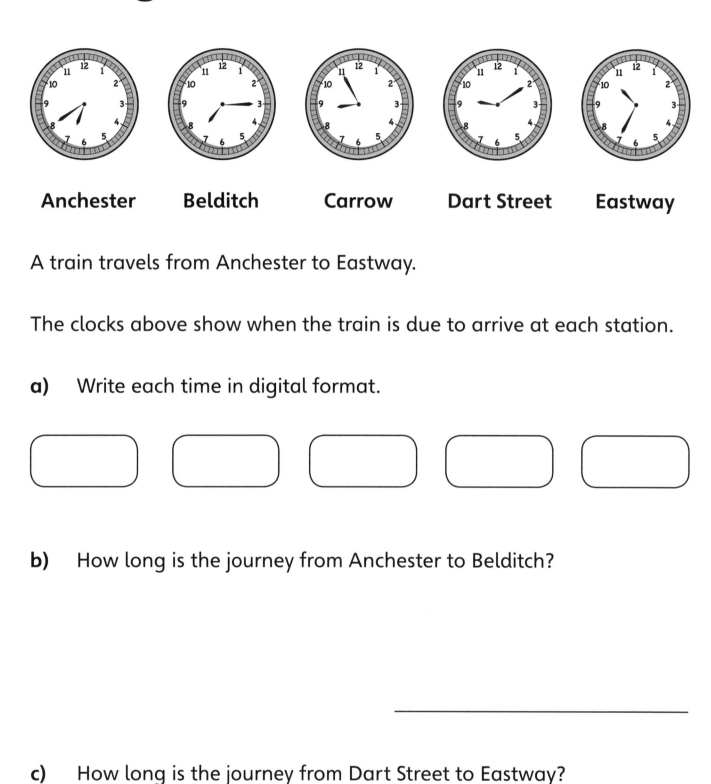

| Anchester | Belditch | Carrow | Dart Street | Eastway |

A train travels from Anchester to Eastway.

The clocks above show when the train is due to arrive at each station.

a)   Write each time in digital format.

⬭   ⬭   ⬭   ⬭   ⬭

b)   How long is the journey from Anchester to Belditch?

_____

c)   How long is the journey from Dart Street to Eastway?

_____

Champions' Challenge

The train was running 80 minutes late. What time did it stop at each station?

Anchester

Belditch

Carrow

Dart Street

Eastway

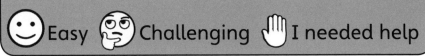

I found this:
☺ Easy 🤔 Challenging ✋ I needed help

Have you mastered...?

doubling and halving 3-digit numbers

a) Use partitioning to double these numbers:

142

374

469

b) Use partitioning to halve these numbers:

648

476

508

12

Champions' Challenge

1) Which is greater, double £235 or half of £940? How do you know?

_____

2) Invent a problem where doubling one number and halving another gives the same answer.

_____

_____

_____

3) Tanya doubles a number twice to get 940. What was her number?

I found this:

☺ Easy 🤔 Challenging ✋ I needed help

adding 3-digit numbers in columns

Here is Bill's homework. Check each answer using column addition. Is each answer right or wrong? Tick or cross each one.

a)   482 + 243 = 625

b)   328 + 556 = 884

c)   739 + 187= 916

d)   275 + 556 = 721

Champions' Challenge

Circle the sum you think will give the largest total.

356 + 827

37 + 679 + 585

296 + 607 + 364

Set them out and find each answer to check your prediction.

 I found this:
 Easy  Challenging 🖐 I needed help

15

Have you mastered...?
finding tenths

a) Match the fractions to the decimal equivalents.

b) What is:

43 ÷ 10

562 ÷ 10

3 ÷ 10

Champions' Challenge

1) Answer these six questions and write the answers in order from smallest to largest.

$3\frac{3}{10}$ as a decimal $42 \div 10$ $4\frac{1}{2}$ as a decimal

$0{\cdot}9 \times 10$ $\frac{6}{10}$ as a decimal $7 \div 10$

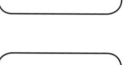

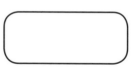

2) Write the decimal number that comes halfway between $\frac{1}{2}$ and $\frac{6}{10}$.

I found this:

 Easy   Challenging I needed help

Have you mastered...?
converting measures

a) Write the mass shown on each scale in kg, then in grams.

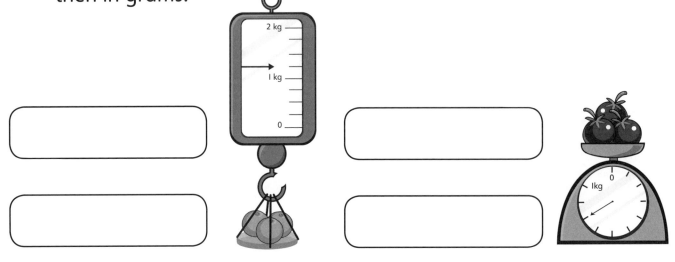

b) Fill in the correct symbol, <, > or = for each pair.

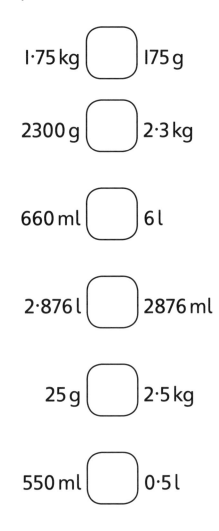

1·75 kg ⬚ 175 g

2300 g ⬚ 2·3 kg

660 ml ⬚ 6 l

2·876 l ⬚ 2876 ml

25 g ⬚ 2·5 kg

550 ml ⬚ 0·5 l

Champions' Challenge

1) Which is more, five cups that each hold 50 ml, or a bottle holding 0·2 litres?

_____

2) Which of these items can you weigh with balance scales and the four weights: 10 g, 100 g, 500 g and 1 kg?

$1\frac{1}{2}$ kg of apples   560 g of peas $\frac{3}{4}$ kg of rice   0·6 kg of potatoes

_____

_____

_____

_____

I found this:

 Easy Challenging I needed help

19

Have you mastered...?

counting up to solve subtraction

a) For each number, how many more to the next hundred?

57

378

239

127

b) Use counting up on a number line to solve:

243 – 186

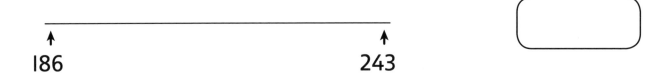

186   243

462 – 285

285   462

Champions' Challenge

1) There are 312 steps to get to the top of a tower. Maya has walked up 167. Use counting up to work out how many more steps to the top.

2) A jug holds 765 ml of water. If there are already 480 ml in it, use counting up to work out how much more is needed to fill it up.

3) Hari has counted up 154 and reached a number between 500 and 510. His starting number has a units digit of 8. What number is it likely to be?

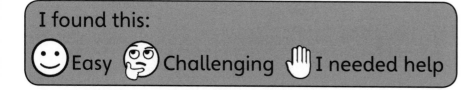

I found this:

☺ Easy 🤔 Challenging ✋ I needed help

multiplying with a grid

a)   Complete this grid to solve 4 × 243.

×	200	40	3
4			

b)   Use a grid to solve:

3 × 327

6 × 165

Champions' Challenge

On this grid, circle two mistakes then work out the correct answer to 6 × 374.

×	300	70	4
6	180	420	36

×	400		9
8		480	

On this grid, find the missing numbers then work out the answer.

I found this:

 Easy 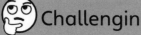 Challenging  I needed help

Have you mastered...?
rounding 3- and 4-digit numbers

a) Is each statement true or false? (Circle T for true, or F for false.)
If it is false, explain what is wrong and find the correct answer.

229 to the nearest 10 is 300.   T / F

_____

449 to the nearest 100 is 500.   T / F

_____

4505 to the nearest 1000 is 5000.   T / F

_____

6777 to the nearest 100 is 6700.   T / F

_____

b) Draw a number line from 3000 to 4000. Mark these numbers on it in approximately the right place.

3500   3900   3200   3050

Champions' Challenge

1) Peter says that there are 100 whole numbers that round to 500 when written to the nearest 100 (including the number 500 itself). Is he right?

_____

_____

2) How many numbers round to 600 to the nearest 100?

_____

_____

How many numbers round to 6000 to the nearest 1000?

_____

_____

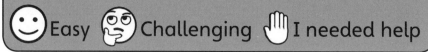

I found this:

☺ Easy 🤔 Challenging ✋ I needed help

Have you mastered...?

adding and subtracting multiples of 1, 10 and 100

a) Use a mental method to solve:

3523 + 400

8683 – 60

3523 + 120

9858 – 307

6460 + 700

4672 + 199

b) Peter has 1623 stickers. His friend gives him 160 stickers. How many does he have now?

c) Maria counts on in 25s from 202. What number does she get to after counting on five 25s?

d) Ahmed counts back in 25s from 1869. What number does he get to after counting back seven 25s?

Champions' Challenge

1) Peter says that if he counts in 25s from 237 the 1s digit will always be a 7 or a 2. Is he right?

_____

2) How many 25s does Peter count on from 237 until he goes past 1000? How do you know?

3) James counts back in 25s. He is now at 339. What 3-digit numbers between 500 and 600 might he have started from? Show how you are sure.

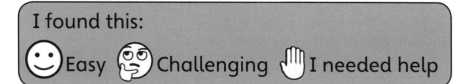

I found this:

😊 Easy 🤔 Challenging ✋ I needed help

27

Have you mastered...?
solving problems with fractions

a) Find these fractions:

$\frac{3}{4}$ of 24

$\frac{5}{6}$ of 18

$\frac{2}{3}$ of 39

$\frac{3}{5}$ of 150

b) Peter missed the lesson on solving problems. How would you help him solve this problem?

Ahmed collected 25 conkers. He gave $\frac{2}{5}$ of the conkers to his brother. How many conkers has he got left?

_____

_____

_____

_____

What is the answer to the problem?

c) If $\frac{3}{4}$ of a number is 15, what is the number?

 # Champions' Challenge

1) $\frac{2}{3}$ of a number is 16. What is the number?

Is $\frac{3}{4}$ of that number more or less than $\frac{2}{3}$ of it?

_____

2) Maya has £100. She spends $\frac{2}{5}$ of her money on a computer game. She then spends $\frac{3}{4}$ of the remaining money on a present for her sister. How much does she now have left?

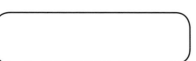

I found this:

Easy Challenging I needed help

Have you mastered...?
finding equivalent fractions

a) These pairs of fractions are equivalent fractions. True or false? In each case, explain your answer.

$\dfrac{2}{3} = \dfrac{5}{6}$ _____

_____

$\dfrac{3}{8} = \dfrac{6}{16}$ _____

_____

$\dfrac{1}{4} = \dfrac{3}{12}$ _____

_____

$\dfrac{3}{5} = \dfrac{15}{20}$ _____

_____

b) Write each of these fractions in its simplest form.

$\dfrac{16}{20}$

$\dfrac{18}{24}$

$\dfrac{20}{30}$

Champions' Challenge

1) In each case, identify the odd one out and explain why.

$\frac{12}{16}$ $\frac{3}{4}$ $\frac{20}{28}$ $\frac{15}{20}$

_____

$\frac{9}{15}$ $\frac{15}{25}$ $\frac{35}{50}$ $\frac{3}{5}$

_____

$\frac{15}{18}$ $\frac{10}{15}$ $\frac{22}{33}$ $\frac{6}{9}$

_____

2) Make up another problem like this for your friends to solve.

I found this:

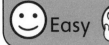 Easy   Challenging   I needed help

Have you mastered...?
acute and obtuse angles

a) Are these angles acute or obtuse?

35° _____   130° _____

95° _____   75° _____

How do you know?

_____

b) Put these five angles in order of size, starting with the smallest:

A right angle   _____

An angle of 30°   _____

An angle of 99°   _____

Half a right angle   _____

An angle of 130°   _____

c) On these shapes label each angle as an acute angle, an obtuse angle or a right angle.

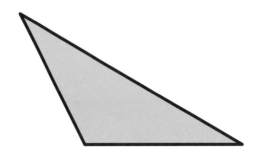

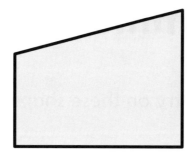

Champions' Challenge

1) Draw a triangle with a right angle. What can you say about the other two angles? Why is this true for all right-angled triangles?

_____

_____

2) Is it possible to draw a triangle with two obtuse angles? Explain your answer.

_____

_____

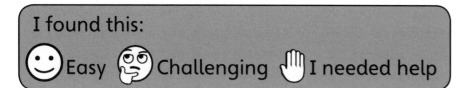

I found this:

☺ Easy 🤔 Challenging ✋ I needed help

Have you mastered...?
identifying symmetry in shapes

a)   Mark any lines of symmetry on these shapes.
Check with a mirror!

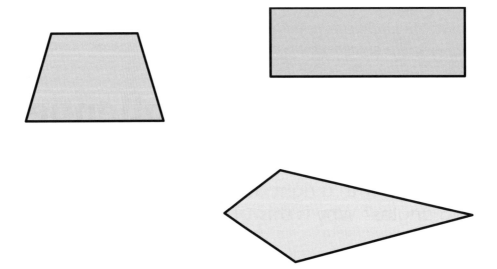

b)   Complete each shape with its reflection in the dotted mirror line.

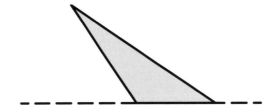

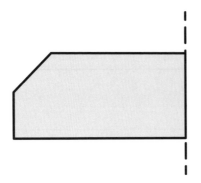

Champions' Challenge

1) Draw three triangles, one with no lines of symmetry, one with one line of symmetry and one with three lines of symmetry.
Name each triangle.

_____

_____

_____

2) Is it possible to draw a triangle with two lines of symmetry?

_____

I found this:

☺ Easy 🤔 Challenging ✋ I needed help

dividing 2- and 3-digit numbers

a) Work these out:

240 ÷ 6

320 ÷ 4

b) Solve these divisions:

83 ÷ 5

112 ÷ 8

123 ÷ 9

We can divide by 4 by halving twice.
Use this to solve the next two questions.

c) How many cars can be made with 84 wheels?

d)   A carpenter makes 76 table legs. How many tables is that?

Champions' Challenge

1)   A farmer has 140 eggs. He puts them into boxes of six.
How many boxes can he fill? How many eggs are left over?

2)   How many boxes could he fill if he had 280 eggs?

How many could he fill if he had 420 eggs?

3)   How many numbers between 80 and 120 will give a remainder
of 5 when divided by 7?

I found this:

Easy Challenging I needed help

Have you mastered...?
all the multiplication and division facts

a) Solve these multiplications and divisions.

7 × 6   56 ÷ 7

81 ÷ 9   48 ÷ 4

9 × 8   48 ÷ 6

b) What is:

30 × 4    4 × 800

5 × 700   7 × 70

90 × 4   30 × 80

c) Find all the factor pairs for 24 and for 32.

24: _____

32: _____

d) Peter says that 12 × 3 is the same as 9 × 4. Is he right?

_____

_____

e)   Write two pairs of multiplication facts that have the same answer. Don't use the number 1.

_____

f)   Write three multiplication facts that all have the same answer. Don't use the number 1.

_____

Champions' Challenge

1)   Jill says that 20 has eight factors. Is she right?   _____
What are the factors of 20?

_____

2)   Mary says that 16 has five factors. Is she right?   _____
What are the factors of 16?

_____

3)   Find four more numbers with an odd number of factors. What can you say about these numbers?

_____

I found this:

☺ Easy   🤔 Challenging   ✋ I needed help

Have you mastered...?
addition methods

a) Set out and solve these.

4578 + 3716

3375 + 8636

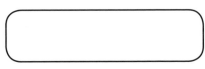

4826 + 748 + 78

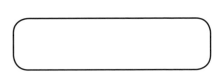

b) Find the total cost of three pairs of shoes, costing £65, £48 and £79.

c) Four large parcels have masses 67 kg, 53 kg, 82 kg and 46 kg. What is their total mass?

d) Two amounts total £100. Both end 50p. No digit is used twice other than 5 and 0. What can the amounts be?

[ ]

[ ]

Champions' Challenge

1) Three of these numbers added together total 10 000. Which three are they?

3641   4172   2106   3456   4655   4253

[ ]

[ ]

[ ]

2) Find three more 4-digit numbers that will total 10 000. Each number should have a different ones (unit) digit.

[ ]

[ ]

[ ]

I found this:
☺ Easy 🤔 Challenging ✋ I needed help

41

Have you mastered...?
different subtraction methods

a) Solve these by counting up on a number line.

2000 – 1590

[   ]

4000 – 1968

[   ]

304 – 267

[   ]

5100 – 4650

[   ]

b) Set out and solve these.

734 – 262

[   ]

923 – 147

[   ]

In a computer game Cyril scores 1862 points, Cherry scores 678 and Sidney scores 382.

c) What is the difference between the scores of Sidney and Cherry?

d) How many more points did Cyril score than Cherry?

Champions' Challenge

1) Find two numbers that have a total of more than 10 000 and a difference of less than 1000.

_____

2) Find two numbers that have a total of between 9000 and 10 000 and a difference of between 1000 and 2000.

_____

I found this:

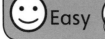 Easy  Challenging I needed help

Have you mastered...?
converting clock times

a) Put these seven times in order, starting with the earliest.

4:35pm   4:30am   04:00   Midday   16:00   14:35   6pm

_____

_____

b) These clocks all show pm times. Write them as digital 24-hour clock times.

c) The swimming lesson starts at 13:45 and lasts for 35 minutes. What time does it finish?

Champions' Challenge

The table shows part of a bus timetable. The bus takes 23 minutes to travel from the Fire Station to the Garden Centre, and 26 minutes from the Garden Centre to the High Street.

I) Complete the timetable in both 12- and 24-hour clock times.

	Fire Station	Garden Centre	High Street	Island Wall
12-hour clock time		12:18pm		1:03pm
24-hour clock time		12:18		

2) How long does it take to travel from the High Street to Island Wall?

_____

I found this:

 Easy Challenging ✋ I needed help

45

Have you mastered...?
solving addition and subtraction problems

Cafe price list

Sausage £2·35   Chips £1·40   Drinks £1·80

a)   How much does two sausages and one portion of chips cost?

b)   How much change will I get from £5 if I buy chips and a drink?

c)   How much more does it cost for a sausage than a drink?

d)   The length of the café is 8·45 m and its width is 4·80 m. What is the difference between its length and its width?

Champions' Challenge

1) How much would it cost for 10 people to each have a sausage, chips and a drink?

2) The length of the café is increased by 180 cm. What is its new length in metres?

3) Each bag of chips has mass 220 grams. What is the mass of 12 bags in kilograms?

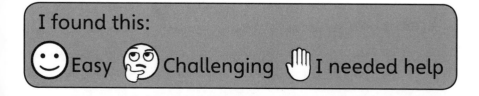

I found this:

:) Easy   Challenging   I needed help

Have you mastered...?
negative numbers

a) Put these numbers in order from smallest to largest:

3   ⁻4   ⁻1   5   ⁻6   2

_____

b) Find the difference in temperature between the two numbers in each pair.

⁻3°C and 2°C

⁻7°C and ⁻3°C

⁻1°C and 1°C

c) The temperature in Finland is ⁻7°C and in Spain it is 5°C. What is the difference between these temperatures? Draw a picture of a thermometer to explain the answer to a friend.

Champions' Challenge

1) Can you find four pairs of temperatures that have a difference of 9°C? In each case one temperature should be above zero and the other should be below zero.

2) In Sweden it is ⁻6°C, in Russia it is ⁻1°C and in England it is 3°C. By how many degrees does the temperature need to increase in each country to reach 10°C?

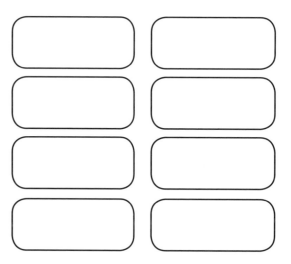

Sweden

Russia

England

I found this:

☺ Easy 🤔 Challenging ✋ I needed help

Have you mastered...?
mental multiplication and division

a) Solve the following:

8 × 12

72 ÷ 12

132 ÷ 11

2 × 7 × 3

12 × 0

7 × 8 × 2

b) Work out:

30 × 12

7700 ÷ 11

11 × 60

Double 27

480 ÷ 12

Half 68

c) Peter says he can find 14 × 4 by doubling and doubling again. Is he right? What is the answer?

_____

Can you find the answer to 23 × 4 using this method?

_____

How can you check these answers by halving?

_____

Champions' Challenge

A good way to multiply by 12 is to find 10 times and 2 times and then add them together.

1) Use this method to multiply by 13, 14, 16, 17 and 18.

8 × 13

9 × 14

7 × 16

8 × 18

6 × 17

12 × 13

2) How can you check these answers?

_____

I found this:

 Easy 😖 Challenging ✋ I needed help

51

Have you mastered...?
setting out and solving multiplication problems

For each of these problems, first write down your estimate, then find the answer and then check your answer.

a) A laptop costs £523. How much would four laptops cost?

estimate: [   ]

[   ]

b) Fido eats six dog biscuits every day. How many is that in a year (365 days)?

estimate: [   ]

[   ]

c) Cinema tickets cost £6·35. If seven friends go, how much will they pay altogether?

estimate: [   ]

[   ]

Champions' Challenge

I)   Use the digits 4, 5, 6 and 7 in the following equation to give the largest possible product and the smallest possible product

⬭⬭⬭ × ⬭ = ⬭

⬭⬭⬭ × ⬭ = ⬭

2)   Now try this with four different digits where one of them is 0.

⬭⬭⬭ × ⬭ = ⬭

⬭⬭⬭ × ⬭ = ⬭

I found this:

 Easy Challenging I needed help

53

Have you mastered...?
finding the area and perimeter of shapes

a) Find the area and perimeter of these two shapes.

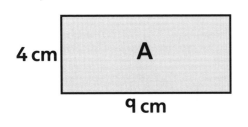

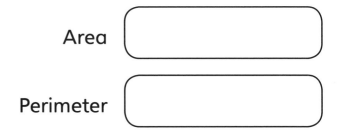

Area

Perimeter

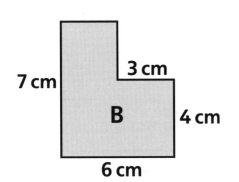

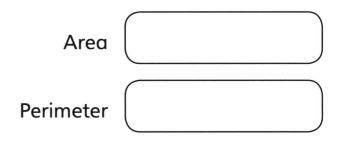

Area

Perimeter

A rectangle has an area of 36 cm². Its length is 12 cm.

b) What is its width?

c) What is its perimeter?

Champions' Challenge

1) Rectangle C is 12 cm long and 6 cm wide. Rectangle D has twice the area of Rectangle C. What could its length and its width be? Find at least three different answers.

_____

_____

_____

2) A square has a perimeter of 32 cm. What is its area? Why did you only need one piece of information to solve this?

_____

_____

_____

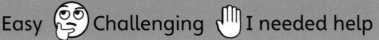

I found this:

☺ Easy 🤔 Challenging ✋ I needed help

55

Have you mastered...?
properties of shapes

Write true or false for each statement. Write what is wrong with the statements that are false. In each case explain your answer – you can draw pictures of the shapes to help.

a)   A hexagon has twice as many sides as a quadrilateral.

_____

_____

b)   A kite has one line of symmetry.

_____

_____

c)   The faces of a cuboid are all squares.

_____

_____

d)   All the angles of a scalene triangle are equal.

_____

_____

e)   Triangles are never symmetrical.

_____

_____

f) A cone is the only shape that has a circle as a face.

_____

 # Champions' Challenge

1) Draw a pentagon with three right angles and a line of symmetry.

2) Make up your own true or false quiz about these shapes.

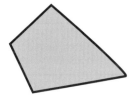   

_____

_____

_____

I found this: Easy Challenging I needed help

57

Have you mastered...?

counting and solving problems with decimals

a) Write the next three numbers in these decimal counting sequences:

3·6, 3·7, 3·8, [　　], [　　], [　　]

5·84, 5·83, 5·82, [　　], [　　], [　　]

b) Solve these:

7·3 – 0·1   [　　]   3·65 – 0·01   [　　]

5·27 + 0·01   [　　]   6·82 + 0·1   [　　]

14·7 + 0·1   [　　]

c) A frog jumps 1·53 m then a further 18 cm. How far does the frog jump altogether?

[　　]

d) Peter has £3·48. He finds a 20p coin and a 5p coin. How much does he now have?

[　　]

e) How can you check your answers to questions **c)** and **d)**?

_____

Champions' Challenge

1) Find the number or measure that is exactly half way between the following pairs:

4·56 and 4·76	
17·28 and 17·78	
5·8 m and 620 cm	
270p and £3·44	
13·36 m and 1388 cm	
3·2 and 3·9	

2) Choose the trickiest two and explain how you found the answers.

_____

_____

_____

I found this:

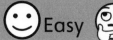 Easy 🤔 Challenging ✋ I needed help

Have you mastered...?

mastered simplifying and comparing fractions

a) Write at least four fractions that are equivalent to $\frac{1}{2}$. How can you be sure they are all equivalent?

b) Write these fractions in their simplest form:

$\frac{3}{12}$ $\frac{8}{10}$ $\frac{18}{24}$ $\frac{20}{30}$ $\frac{12}{20}$

c) Which three of these are equal to $\frac{1}{3}$?

$\frac{3}{9}$ $\frac{5}{16}$ $\frac{2}{6}$ $\frac{4}{12}$ $\frac{7}{18}$

d) How can you check your answers?

Champions' Challenge

1) Look at your answers to question **(c)**. Use your answers to write three fractions which are equivalent to $\frac{2}{3}$.

2) In the pairs below, which is the larger fraction? How can you use the idea of equivalent fractions to explain your answers?

$\frac{12}{20}$ or $\frac{4}{5}$

$\frac{6}{16}$ or $\frac{1}{4}$

$\frac{11}{12}$ or $\frac{5}{6}$

$\frac{2}{3}$ or $\frac{3}{4}$

$\frac{1}{6}$ or $\frac{2}{9}$

_____

_____

_____

I found this:

 Easy Challenging I needed help

Have you mastered...?
mental addition using place value and number facts

Solve these mentally!

a) What must be added to each of these numbers to make 200?

178 [ ]   33 [ ]

146 [ ]   19 [ ]

85 [ ]

b) What is 55 more than each of these numbers?

28 [ ]   1438 [ ]

428 [ ]   4438 [ ]

438 [ ]

c) Sunil has 178 marbles and James has 48 marbles. How many marbles do they have altogether?

[ ]

d) Tara has collected £125? from a sponsored silence. Her sister Sara has collected £53. How much more do they need together to reach their joint target of £200?

[ ]

e) For questions (c) and (d), how can you check your answers?

_____

_____

 # Champions' Challenge

I) Find two sets of three numbers that total 200.

| 19 | 28 | 37 | 45 | 54 | 62 |

| 69 | 77 | 78 | 81 | 85 | 92 |

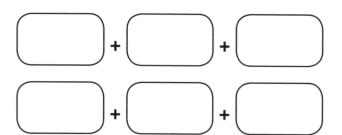

2) Find two more sets of three numbers that total 200. Each of the three numbers should have a different digit in the 10s and the 1s place.

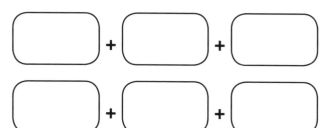

I found this:

 Easy Challenging ✋ I needed help

Have you mastered...?

solving problems using multiplication and factors

a) Solve these using doubling and halving methods, showing how you solved the problems.

26 × 4

18 × 8

164 ÷ 4

168 ÷ 8

b) Jane says that to multiply by 6 you can multiply by 3 and double. Use this method to solve:

23 × 6

41 × 6

c) How can you check your answers?

d) Use this method to find out how many eggs there are in 32 boxes of 6 eggs.

Champions' Challenge

1) How could you multiply a number by 12 by using the factors of 12?

_____

_____

2) Try out your method to find:

14 × 12

22 × 12

31 × 12

3) How can you check your answers?

_____

_____

I found this:

 Easy Challenging 🖐 I needed help

Have you mastered...?

solving and checking subtraction problems

Solve these subtraction problems, choosing the best method – counting up on a number line or column subtraction.

a) Nadia has collected 310 stickers. She gives 185 away to her friends. How many does she have left?

b) Two containers are filled with juice. One holds 2846 ml, the other 3673 ml. What is the difference in capacity between the containers?

c) Andrew buys a book for £14·75. How much change will he get from £20?

d) Choose one of the questions and check your answer using addition.

Champions' Challenge

1) Use counting up on a number line to solve 3000 – 1646.

2) Use column subtraction to solve 5212 – 3858.

3) What do you notice about your answers?

_____

4) Two more subtraction questions each give an answer of 2627. Make up two subtraction questions that give this answer, one that is best solved using counting up on a number line and one that is best solved by column subtraction.

_____

_____

I found this:

Easy 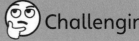Challenging 🤚I needed help

Have you mastered...?
using coordinates

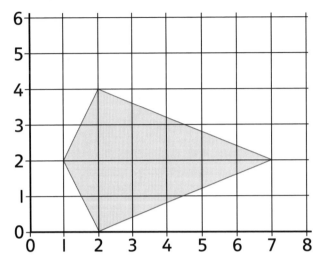

a) What are the four coordinates of the corners of this shape?

_____

b) If the shape is moved two squares up, what will the new coordinates be?

_____

c) Plot these points and use a ruler and sharp pencil to join them:

(2, 1), (6, 1) and (2, 5)

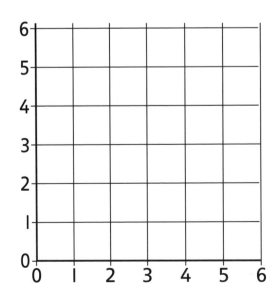

d) What shape is this?

_____

 **Champions' Challenge**

1) Two coordinates of a parallelogram are (1, 2) and (2, 4). Plot these points and complete a parallelogram. What are the coordinates of the other two corners?

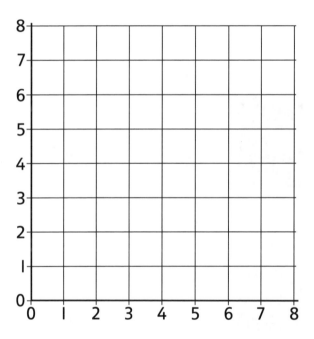

_____

2) Now imagine your parallelogram is moved three squares to the right. What are its new coordinates?

_____

I found this:

Easy 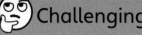Challenging I needed help

Have you mastered...?
using information in a bar chart

This graph shows the number of house points scored.

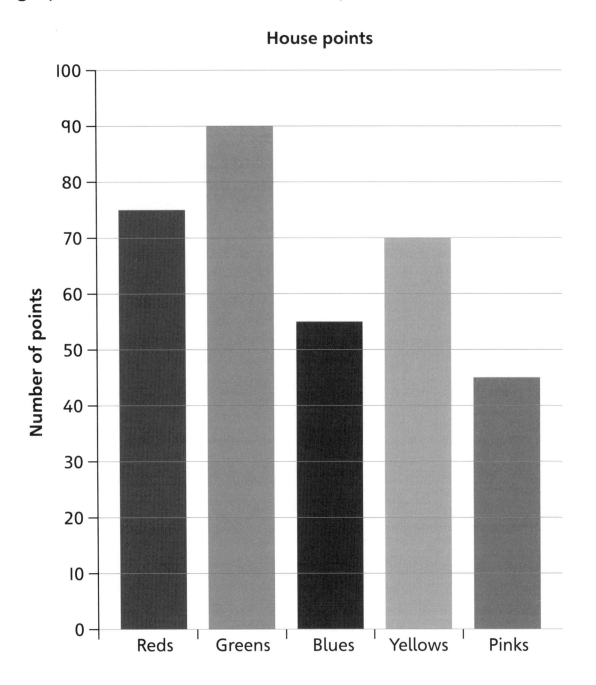

House points

a)   How many more points did the Greens score than the Pinks?

b) What was the total of the Reds' and the Blues' points?

c) Which house scored the third highest number of points?

_____

d) How many points would the Blues need to equal the Yellows?

e) How many house points were awarded altogether?

f) Make up two more questions for your friends to answer.

1. _____

_____

_____

2. _____

_____

_____

I found this:

 Easy 😵 Challenging ✋ I needed help

Continues on next page

using information in a bar chart

This graph shows the number of house points scored.

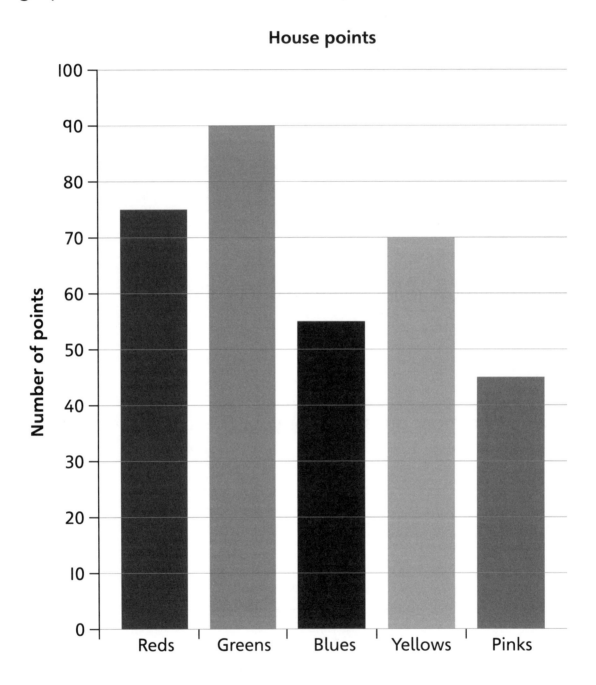

House points

Champions' Challenge

1) Peter says that the Pinks and the Reds together totalled more points than the Blues and the Yellows together.
Is he correct?

_____

_____

2) Parvati says that she is sure without adding up that the total points scored by the five teams is less than 450.
How could she be sure of this without adding?

_____

_____

_____

_____

3) Maya says that the smallest difference is between the Blues and the Pinks. Is she correct?

_____

_____

I found this:

☺ Easy 🤔 Challenging ✋ I needed help

Have you mastered...?

adding and subtracting fractions

a) Work out these additions and subtractions:

$\frac{3}{5} + \frac{1}{5}$

$\frac{7}{12} + \frac{2}{12}$

$\frac{9}{10} - \frac{3}{10}$

$\frac{7}{9} + \frac{2}{9}$

b) Sharif eats $\frac{7}{10}$ of a pizza, Maria eats $\frac{9}{10}$ of a pizza.
How much pizza do they eat altogether?

How much more pizza does Maria eat than Sharif?

c) Circle the three fraction pairs that total 1. How do you know?

$\frac{4}{6} + \frac{3}{6}$ $\frac{5}{7} + \frac{2}{7}$ $\frac{3}{9} + \frac{5}{9}$ $\frac{4}{10} + \frac{6}{10}$ $\frac{1}{4} + \frac{6}{8}$

_____

_____

Champions' Challenge

1) Write four more pairs of fractions that total 1. Can you write at least two examples where the two fractions have different denominators?

2) What fraction can be added to each of these pairs to make 1?

$\frac{2}{7} + \frac{4}{7}$ $\frac{3}{8} + \frac{1}{8}$ $\frac{4}{12} + \frac{1}{2}$ $\frac{1}{3} + \frac{5}{9}$

I found this:

Easy Challenging I needed help

Have you mastered...?

multiplying and dividing decimals

a) Put these eight numbers in order, smallest to largest:

5·8   6·17   5·84   6·99   6·71   6·08   6·7   5·48

_____

_____

b) Maya rounds each of the numbers in question **(a)** to the nearest whole number. She says that only three of them round to 6. Is she right? Which numbers do round to 6?

_____

_____

c) Solve these:

36 ÷ 10	
1·4 × 10	
523 ÷ 100	
0·7 × 100	
3·42 ÷ 10	

Champions' Challenge

1) Ahmed divides these numbers by 10 then multiplies them by 100. What number does he get in each case?

36

12·1

471

0·9

6·3

2) Compare the answers to the starting numbers. What do you notice? What would be a shortcut to dividing by 10 then multiplying by 100? Check this for five more numbers.

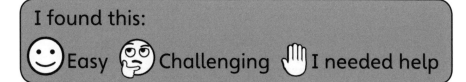

I found this:

☺ Easy   🤔 Challenging   ✋ I needed help

Have you mastered...?
finding fractional amounts

a) Five friends share equally a lottery prize of £75. How much do they each get?

b) In each case below, which is the larger prize?
Explain how you know for each pair.

$\frac{1}{4}$ of £84 or $\frac{1}{5}$ of £100

_____

_____

$\frac{2}{3}$ of £96 or $\frac{3}{4}$ of £88

_____

_____

$\frac{5}{8}$ of £120 or $\frac{4}{5}$ of £90

_____

_____

c) How would you explain to a friend who has been away how to find a fraction of any amount?

_____

_____

Champions' Challenge

1) Which is larger, $\frac{3}{8}$ of £96 or $\frac{1}{4}$ of £144?

_____

2) Find three different pairs of fractional amounts that result in the same answer.

_____

_____

_____

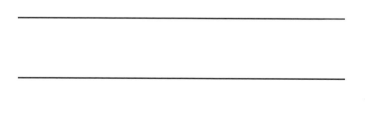

I found this:

☺ Easy 🤔 Challenging ✋ I needed help

Date: _____

Things to find out

When you start a new topic, you will have lots of questions and things you are not sure about. Record your thoughts here.

What would you like to find out?

What skills would you like to practise?

What new skills would you like to learn?

What questions would you like answering?

Explaining my learning

Imagine that a new superhero, Mighty Maths Girl, wants to use her superpowers to make everyone in the world understand maths. She comes to your classroom for help.

How would you explain your maths work to her?

Date: _____

My dictionary

There are lots of important words we need to remember when it comes to maths. This is your maths dictionary where you can record key mathematical words and their meanings.

Give an example to help you remember each word. Use pictures, models, questions or word problems to help you.

Word	Meaning	Example

Date: _____

My challenges

As you learn a new topic, you will encounter lots of different challenges along the way. Overcoming these challenges helps to deepen your understanding.

What challenges have you faced during your maths learning? Why were these challenges important? How did you overcome them?

Date: _____

Real-life maths

What we learn in maths helps us in our everyday lives. Can you think of how what you have learnt in maths can be used in real life?

Think about any activities you usually do such as watching television, eating lunch, playing sport, or walking to school.

Real-life context	How I could use maths

Date: _____

Making mistakes

Did you know that we can learn a lot from making mistakes? They help us to move on with our learning.

Think about the mistakes that you have made and why they are important in your maths learning.

Mistakes I have made	Why they are important

Which of your mistakes do you think was the most valuable? How did it help you?

My Mastery

Colour a circle for each skill to show how you feel about it now.

Mastery Checkpoint	Have you mastered...?	More help!	I think I'm OK	I'm the master!	Date
Checkpoint 1 pages 4–5	Place value in 4-digit numbers	◯	◯	◯	
Checkpoint 2 pages 6–7	Times-tables facts	◯	◯	◯	
Checkpoint 3 pages 8–9	Finding fractions of amounts	◯	◯	◯	
Checkpoint 4 pages 10–11	Telling the time	◯	◯	◯	
Checkpoint 5 pages 12–13	Doubling and halving 3-digit numbers	◯	◯	◯	
Checkpoint 6 pages 14–15	Adding 3-digit numbers in columns	◯	◯	◯	
Checkpoint 7 pages 16–17	Finding tenths	◯	◯	◯	

Colour a circle for each skill to show how you feel about it now.

Mastery Checkpoint	Have you mastered...?	More help!	I think I'm OK	I'm the master!	Date
Checkpoint 8 pages 18–19	Converting measures	○	○	○	
Checkpoint 9 pages 20–21	Counting up to solve subtraction	○	○	○	
Checkpoint 10 pages 22–23	Multiplying with a grid	○	○	○	
Checkpoint 11 pages 24–25	Rounding 3 and 4-digit numbers	○	○	○	
Checkpoint 12 pages 26–27	Adding and subtracting multiples of 1, 10 and 100	○	○	○	
Checkpoint 13 pages 28–29	Solving problems with fractions	○	○	○	

My Mastery

Colour a circle for each skill to show how you feel about it now.

Mastery Checkpoint	Have you mastered...?	More help!	I think I'm OK	I'm the master!	Date
Checkpoint 14 pages 30–31	Finding equivalent fractions	◯	◯	◯	
Checkpoint 15 pages 32–33	Acute and obtuse angles	◯	◯	◯	
Checkpoint 16 pages 34–35	Identifying symmetry in shapes	◯	◯	◯	
Checkpoint 17 pages 36–37	Dividing 2- and 3-digit numbers	◯	◯	◯	
Checkpoint 18 pages 38–39	All the multiplication and division facts	◯	◯	◯	
Checkpoint 19 pages 40–41	Addition methods	◯	◯	◯	

Colour a circle for each skill to show how you feel about it now.

Mastery Checkpoint	Have you mastered...?	More help!	I think I'm OK	I'm the master!	Date
Checkpoint 20 pages 42–43	Different subtraction methods	◯	◯	◯	
Checkpoint 21 pages 44–45	Converting clock times	◯	◯	◯	
Checkpoint 22 pages 46–47	Solving addition and subtraction problems	◯	◯	◯	
Checkpoint 23 pages 48–49	Negative numbers	◯	◯	◯	
Checkpoint 24 pages 50–51	Mental multiplication and division	◯	◯	◯	
Checkpoint 25 pages 52–53	Setting out and solving multiplication problems	◯	◯	◯	

My Mastery

Colour a circle for each skill to show how you feel about it now.

Mastery Checkpoint	Have you mastered...?	More help!	I think I'm OK	I'm the master!	Date
Checkpoint 26 pages 54–55	Finding the area and perimeter of shapes	◯	◯	◯	
Checkpoint 27 pages 56–57	Properties of shapes	◯	◯	◯	
Checkpoint 28 pages 58–59	Counting and solving problems with decimals	◯	◯	◯	
Checkpoint 29 pages 60–61	Simplifying and comparing fractions	◯	◯	◯	
Checkpoint 30 pages 62–63	Mental addition using place value and number facts	◯	◯	◯	
Checkpoint 31 pages 64–65	Solving problems using multiplication and factors	◯	◯	◯	

Colour a circle for each skill to show how you feel about it now.

Mastery Checkpoint	Have you mastered…?	More help!	I think I'm OK	I'm the master!	Date
Checkpoint 32 pages 66–67	Solving and checking subtraction problems	◯	◯	◯	
Checkpoint 33 pages 68–69	Using coordinates	◯	◯	◯	
Checkpoint 34 pages 70–73	Using information in a bar chart	◯	◯	◯	
Checkpoint 35 pages 74–75	Adding and subtracting fractions	◯	◯	◯	
Checkpoint 36 pages 76–77	Multiplying and dividing decimals	◯	◯	◯	
Checkpoint 37 pages 78–79	Finding fractional amounts	◯	◯	◯	

Checkpoints ordered by curriculum domain

Number – number and place value		
Checkpoint 1	Place value in 4-digit numbers	4–5
Checkpoint 11	Rounding 3 and 4-digit numbers	24–25
Checkpoint 12	Adding and subtracting multiples of 1, 10 and 100	26–27
Checkpoint 23	Negative numbers	48–49
Number – addition and subtraction		
Checkpoint 6	Adding 3-digit numbers in columns	14–15
Checkpoint 9	Counting up to solve subtraction	20–21
Checkpoint 19	Addition methods	40–41
Checkpoint 20	Different subtraction methods	42–43
Checkpoint 22*	Solving addition and subtraction problems	46–47
Checkpoint 30	Mental addition using place value and number facts	62–63
Checkpoint 32	Solving and checking subtraction problems	66–67
Number – multiplication and division		
Checkpoint 2	Times-tables facts	6–7
Checkpoint 5	Doubling and halving 3-digit numbers	12–13
Checkpoint 10	Multiplying with a grid	22–23
Checkpoint 17	Dividing 2- and 3-digit numbers	36–37
Checkpoint 18	All the multiplication and division facts	38–39
Checkpoint 24	Mental multiplication and division	50–51
Checkpoint 25	Setting out and solving multiplication problems	52–53
Checkpoint 31	Solving problems using multiplication and factors	64–65
Number – fractions (including decimals)		
Checkpoint 3	Finding fractions of amounts	8–9
Checkpoint 7	Finding tenths	16–17
Checkpoint 13	Solving problems with fractions	28–29
Checkpoint 14	Finding equivalent fractions	30–31
Checkpoint 28*	Counting and solving problems with decimals	58–59
Checkpoint 29	Simplifying and comparing fractions	60–61
Checkpoint 35	Adding and subtracting fractions	74–75
Checkpoint 36	Multiplying and dividing decimals	76–77
Checkpoint 37	Finding fractional amounts	78–79
Measurement		
Checkpoint 4	Telling the time	10–11
Checkpoint 8	Converting measures	18–19
Checkpoint 21	Converting clock times	44–45
Checkpoint 22*	Solving addition and subtraction problems	46–47
Checkpoint 26	Finding the area and perimeter of shapes	54–55
Checkpoint 28*	Counting and solving problems with decimals	58–59
Geometry – properties of shapes		
Checkpoint 15	Acute and obtuse angles	32–33
Checkpoint 16	Identifying symmetry in shapes	34–35
Checkpoint 27	Properties of shapes	56–57
Geometry – position and direction		
Checkpoint 33	Using coordinates	68–69
Statistics		
Checkpoint 34	Using information in a bar chart	70–73

*These Checkpoints fall under more than one domain.